D0966937

STORMALONG GOES A-WHALING

#/0#9

Stormalong
Goes a-Whaling

By DON STEERS

Illustrated by YNGVE EDWARD SODERBERG

Fabulous Stories About Stormalong,
the Paul Bunyan of the Sea

The PEQUOT PRESS, Inc.
Stonington   Connecticut

Copyright 1966 by
B. MacDonald Steers
All rights reserved

Library of Congress Catalog Card No. 66-22116

Designed and Illustrated by Yngve Edward Soderberg

Printed by the Stonington Publishing Company

Contents

STORMALONG

STORMALONG was as real as a dream, and dreams are real, aren't they? He was as real as Paul Bunyan, or Santa Claus, or Robin Hood, or the Cardiff Giant.

There is no end to the tales that can be told about him, for he was a restless fellow and went from one experience to another, one ship to another, because ordinary men's lives never seemed to satisfy him.

Just as his big arms never failed of their strength, so his big heart had room in it for all his shipmates, and for all the smaller creatures whose strength was less than his own.

He had Yankee shrewdness, but no great mind. His strength was in his muscles and in his heart. He was as American as johnnycake, as simple and natural as a puppy, and as dear to the hearts of sailor lads as their own sea-dreams.

He represents all that was best in the American sailorman; and to the men themselves he represented all they would like to have been, but were too small and weak and human to be.

Stormalong's Early Life

STORMALONG was born in a village on the seacoast up in Maine, not far from the spot where Paul Pinewoods Bunyan got his start.

Even as a baby he could swim around in the sea as slick as an eel in a keg of oysters. His father was the first Yankee skipper to sail around Cape Horn and all his folks followed the sea.

His great-great-grandfather, Stormy used to say, helped Noah build the Ark and keep it afloat through the flood. "That's writ in my family Bible and no foolin' about it," was the way Stormy put it.

When stormy was a youngster he played along the beach in Maine. He could throw a salt mackerel farther than any other boy, and he thought nothing at all of jumping into the ocean and swimming to the farthest lighthouse. He used to swim a hundred miles or so just to play with the boys on Cape Cod. The boys used to get together and sing a crazy song:

Cape Cod girls, they have no combs —
  Heave away, heave away,
They comb their hair with codfish bones —
  We are bound for Australia!

Cape Cod boys, they have no sleds —
   Heave away, heave away,
They slide down hill on codfish heads —
   We are bound for Australia!

Stormy first wanted to be a pirate, but his father told
him: "Stormy, my lad, pirates is always sure to get
theirselves hanged." So Stormy changed his mind and
decided to be an honest sailor.

He was given a Bible by his mother and, taking his
sea chest under his arm, he signed onto a whaling ship
out of New Bedford called the *Gridiron,* just then
heading out to sea on a five-year whaling voyage. But
the Bible was stolen by a dishonest sailor in a New
Bedford boarding house, and thereafter Stormy had to
steer his own moral course.

We hope the Bible did the other sailor some good.

2

Stormalong as a Young Man

STORMALONG was never a lad of quarrelsome disposition. He was strong and quick to learn, and soon became the most able seaman aboard ship. He told such good yarns to the other sailors at night, down in the fo'c's'le, or stretching their length on deck under the moonlight, that in no time at all he was the favorite of the whole crew.

He could dance pretty well, and old Billy Peg-Leg, the cook, could scratch a fiddle tolerably well, so, in the evening when the moon came up, old Billy would play a sailor's hornpipe, beating time with his wooden leg, and Stormy would start in jigging.

No other man on the ship could shake his legs like Stormy. He lifted them up so high and planted them down on deck with such force that the timbers of the *Gridiron* shivered as if to split. As Stormy danced, he would sing a song at the top of his voice, playing his own accompaniment on a jew's-harp.

By the time Stormy was full-grown, he was a giant in size. He was variously reported to be fourteen fathoms tall, and almost any size you could think of that was big, but a man who knew him personally claims he was

just four fathoms from the deck to the bridge of his nose.

He could whip his weight in sharks. He could crack a cocoanut with one hand. And he was the first sailor to have A.B. after his name; because when he signed it to the articles that first time on the *Gridiron,* it appeared "Stormalong, Alfred Bulltop," for that was his real name.

Foolish folks think "A. B." means able-bodied, but the truth is that ever since the time of Stormalong sailors have been so proud to follow his profession that they have taken his initials as their own. But try as they have, and try as they will, none of them, then or since, have matched or ever will match, Stormy's incredible feats, or even come near them. Stormalong wouldn't care if they did, for he was a true sailor, all four fathoms of him, and always respected his superiors.

And, of course, a sailor always shares everything he has with his shipmates, even his initials, as Stormy did.

3

Stormalong's Appetite

WHEN a whaling ship, or "whaler," had stowed away a thousand gallons of whale-oil, it was the custom to give the men a treat. If the cook was a good-natured fellow, like Billy Peg-Leg, he would make doughnuts and fry them in the last try-pot of oil.

Stormy would never eat more than a hundred of the doughnuts, so as to leave some for his shipmates. This was pretty hard on Stormy, because he liked doughnuts and he had a considerable appetite, when you consider his size. He took his whale soup from a Cape Cod dory; he used a try-pot for a tea cup; ate only ostrich eggs for breakfast; and his favorite meat was shark. His favorite beverage was whale oil or whale milk, cut with good old Maine hard cider.

His appetite was so huge that it finally got so he took Billy Peg-Leg along with him whenever he signed onto a new ship, as his special ship's cook. One of them wouldn't sign on without the other, because Billy was fond of Stormalong and wouldn't be without him, and Stormalong couldn't find any other cook that could keep his stomach satisfied. And, of course, no skipper would take Stormalong onto his ship, when he found out about his appetite, unless he was sure of having a cook that could feed him.

When Stormalong's appetite had been satisfied, he would pick his teeth with a marlin spike (some sailors vowed it was an eighteen-foot oar, but that is an exaggeration). Then he would sing:

Oh, th' times was hard an' th' wages low.
Leave 'er, John-nie, leave 'er.
An' th' grub was bad an' th' gales did blow.
An' it's time for us t' leave 'er!

4

Stormalong Lifts the Anchor

ONCE, when the *Gridiron* was anchored off-shore, a school of whales was sighted.

"They're off on a whale school picnic in charge of their whale schoolteacher," said Stormy.

"Hoist anchor and follow those whales," shouted the Skipper, "and belay that idle chatter."

But when the men rushed off and tried to raise the anchor, they found they could not lift it. They pulled and they hauled and they tugged. It would rise up just a little, then something seemed to catch hold of it and pull it right back to the bottom. At last, when the entire crew bent to the windlass, and Stormy himself put a hand to it to help, they got the anchor near enough to the surface of the water so that they could see down into it a little ways, and there was a pair of wicked-looking eyes staring up at them, and a whole bunch of slimy gray arms wrapped around the anchor.

"Blow me," said Stormy, "if it ain't the biggest octopus I ever see."

The octopus gave a dive and the anchor disappeared again. Stormy drew his knife from his belt, took it between his teeth and was overboard in a jiffy. Stormy went right to the bottom alongside that ocopus, and he was sure a tough looking customer. With four of his slimy arms that stubborn old varmint was hanging onto the

mudhook, and with the other four he was hanging onto the seaweed on the bottom.

All the men on board could see were the signs of the struggle. The water churned and boiled so that the ship rolled as if she were beam to the wind. All Stormy's shipmates were sure their friend had been torn apart. The struggle went on for a quarter of an hour, then Stormy's head came to the surface. Someone called out to throw him a line, but before one could be brought, Stormy had grabbed the anchor chain and came up hand over hand to the deck. The struggling in the water kept on for a while, then died down.

"All right," yelled Stormy. "All hands lean on it and bring it home." Stormy could have done it himself, but he wanted the rest of the crew to have a part in it.

After the anchor was shipped the men all crowded around to learn what had happened.

Stormy said the minute he got down there the old devilfish took two of his arms off the anchor, and two more off the seaweed to which he had been holding on, and twined them around Stormy.

Stormy wrenched himself free, took his knife and fell on his enemy with all the strength he had, which was the same as the force of a wild nor'wester blowing up a tempest.

At last the devilfish had to give in. He just couldn't stand against Stormy. He fell down all worn out and curled up in a heap, too tired out even to get away. Stormy seized the arms of that octopus and tied them up, two by two, in a series of sailor's knots, using double carrick bends.

Some of those knots the monster never was able to undo.

[11]

5

Pelorus Jack

Ever hear of Pelorus Jack? Well, Pelorus Jack was a famous albino porpoise which used to meet all the ships coming into Wellington harbor. Most sailors who ever went to New Zealand have seen and remember Pelorus Jack and swear that he came out to pilot them into the harbor.

Just as you were starting across Cook's Strait, if you looked off your starboard bow, you'd see a big whitish kind of porpoise slipping along ahead of you, arching his back and skipping in and out of the water as graceful and pretty as you please. When your ship had got past the bar across the entrance and well into the harbor, he'd disappear, probably off to meet the next ship.

Well, Pelorus Jack was specially fond of Stormalong because Stormalong loved all innocent and harmless things, in and out of the ocean, and he was specially fond of Pelorus Jack.

Every time the *Gridiron* put into Wellington, old Pelorus was there to meet her and escort her in. Stormalong would throw down some tidbit left over from his dinner, like a chunk of whale steak or something equally fine, and maybe it could be that Pelorus Jack knew there

[13]

was more food on Stormy's ship than on any other. At any rate, old Pelorus never failed to meet Stormy's ship.

But all this came later. Before the *Gridiron* first went into Wellington harbor, Pelorus Jack was just another porpoise and nobody knew anything about him. The *Gridiron* was the first whaleship ever to go into Wellington, and Stormy was on her that voyage. There weren't any charts in those days — at least good ones — and right across the entrance to Wellington harbor was a dangerous bar.

Just as they were going in and heading straight for that shoal, Stormy and the Second Mate were standing their watch at the masthead and Stormy called out: "Hullo there, what's that?"

"Looks like a porpoise," said the Second Mate.

"Palest porpoise I ever did see," said Stormy. "Looks like he needs a heap of good red meat. He looks real peaked."

So Stormy cut off a piece of the whale steak he was munching on and threw it into the water.

The porpoise snapped it up. Then all of a sudden he must have realized where the ship was heading, for he began to cavort around in the water like something crazy. He'd dart toward the ship, then off to starboard and the Second Mate said: "Guess he don't like meat. It's give him indigestion."

"No," says Stormy, "he's tryin' to tell us somethin'."

Then Stormy saw what it was!

"Breakers ahead!" he called.

Sure enough, they were heading straight for a good old-fashioned shipwreck.

"Hard aport," yelled the Captain.

The helmsman brought the wheel around and the ship

swung around that bar, missing it by inches.

"See," said Stormy, "that critter knew what was up."

From that time on Pelorus Jack was Stormy's special favorite, and when the word spread around he was the favorite of every sailor who went into Wellington harbor.

On the *Gridiron* Stormy got the credit for saving the ship and the Captain commended him for the keenness of his observation, but Stormy always gave the credit to Pelorus Jack.

6

Stormalong the Whaleman

STORMALONG was not only a sailorman, he was the best whaleman who ever lived. He could harpoon a whale all by himself, then jump on it and ride along on it bareback till it tired a little, then he'd finish it off with a killing lance. Stormy always got his whale and turned him fin out.

Never hear of Moby Dick any more, do we? That's because Stormy got him and boiled him into lamp oil. Old Captain Ahab hunted the seven seas over for old Moby and finally found him, but he didn't get him, as you remember. It was the other way around.

Well, one day Stormy heard about Captain Ahab and how he lost his leg, and then his life, because of Moby Dick, and it made Stormy real mad. I guess it was the first time in his whole life that Stormy ever lost his temper.

Stormy vowed he'd get that whale, and get him he did. He sighted him one day and knew him right off, for Moby Dick, you recall, was a white whale. Another thing, his spout was like old Ahab had said, "like a shock of wheat" and then, too, many harpoons lay all bent and twisted in his hide, so many ships had tried to get him.

[17]

Well you can bet there was some excitement on the *Gridiron* when Moby Dick was sighted. When all five boats were about to be lowered, Stormy yelled, "Belay there, boys. Let me handle this."

And believe it or not, that day Stormy simply climbed up the rigging a little way, braced his foot against the mainmast, and let go with his harpoon.

He hit that whale square in the small of his back and paralyzed his flukes so that old Moby couldn't thrash around in the water. Neat as a Liverpool splice, it was. Old Moby just lay there, helpless as a worm on a fish-hook, and Stormy could have hauled him in right then, but he didn't. He didn't want to be written down in the ship's log as taking all the credit. He pretended he strained his arm a bit and called out: "Better finish him off, mates, he might come to."

So all five mates of the *Gridiron* lined up against the rail and sunk their irons into him, too. Then, just for courtesy's sake, they let the seamen have a fling at him, too. When they'd finished, Moby Dick looked like a sea-goin' porcupine.

Moby Dick was the only whale ever caught that all the whaleboats and all the mates got credit for, because they all had a hand in his killing, and so it was written down in the log book.

Even before he killed Moby Dick, Stormy's reputation was such that it had reached all the grown-up whales in the ocean. They were so scared of him that whenever it was whispered from one whale to another that Stormy was around, there wasn't a whale to be seen in the whole ocean. They were all down at the bottom, hiding till he passed by.

But when the news about Moby Dick got around, the

other whales figured even the bottom of the ocean wasn't safe. They all took out for the Arctic Ocean, to hide up around the North Pole.

Stormy and the *Gridiron* went right after them. They sailed right through the Arctic Ocean, dodging the floating ice, till the men caught the first glimpse of the Pole sticking up through the snow. Everything would have been all right if they had put their mains'l aback just then and stopped, but they were too greedy for whales, I guess, for they kept going just as if they expected to slip a hawser right around the Pole itself and stay there. Well, they didn't get to the Pole, but stay there they did. With a grinding and crunching and cracking, such as no one had ever heard before, the *Gridiron* stuck fast in the ice. She couldn't move an inch. She was frozen in.

7

Stormalong Gets Out of the Ice

STORMY was down in his bunk taking his usual six months' Arctic winter nap, but the sudden jolt and the noise brought him up on deck. For a while even Stormy was stumped. He tried chipping the ice away with his boarding knife, but the ice up there is thicker than even Stormy's out-size boarding knife was long, so that didn't work. There didn't seem to be much that Stormy could do in a case like this. "Maybe if I had a little breakfast . . ." said Stormy.

That gave Billy Peg-Leg an idea, and nobody but a cook would have thought of such a scheme. "We'll have t' melt thet ice," says Billy. And melt it they did, and this is how they did it.

Billy made up a dory-full of whale-soup, sprinkled it well with a bushel of black pepper and got it good and hot on the galley stove.

While this was simmering, Stormy took his boarding knife and whacked away at the nearest iceberg, and he whacked as if his very life depended on it. Reason was, he was still groggy from his nap and he wanted to get his circulation going. He worked so hard the sweat began to drip off him and froze on its way to the ground. But

[21]

Stormy kept chipping away in the middle of his own hailstorm. Then, when he decided he was hot enough, he drank all the soup with the pepper in it, and between the hot soup, the pepper and the exercise, he had himself in a steaming lather.

Next he lay down on his belly, flat on the deck, hung his head down over the bowsprit, and while the crew set all sail, Stormy blew with all his might.

His hot breath melted a channel right down through the ice floe and the *Gridiron* sailed through into the ice-free waters just as neat as you please.

After which Stormy was a bit winded, so he lay down to finish his nap.

8

Scrimshaw

Ever hear of Scrimshaw? Those things that sailors carve out of whalebone — pie wheels used to crimp the edge of a pie, corset busks for the ladies back home, colored pictures etched on the teeth of the whale, and all that sort of thing?

Well, all the boys on the *Gridiron* spent their spare time making scrimshaw, but Stormy's hands were too big to work with such little things; yet he made a scrimshaw once that topped them all, and this is how he did it.

When the *Gridiron* had gotten out of the ice at the North Pole, she came down toward the Bering Sea. The boys were getting pretty lonesome, but the only houses to be seen anywhere on shore were a few igloos the Eskimos had built, lying huddled around a glacier, or something.

One of the sailors took the Old Man's spy glass to see what the country was like and then he let go with a long, drawn-out whistle, and all the other sailors crowded around begging for a look.

What they saw over there among the igloos was a group of pretty Eskimo girls. They were wrapped in furs

and looked so cozy and cute, like a bunch of little Polar bears, that the men asked the Captain for liberty so they could go ashore and get acquainted.

But first they thought they'd have a little fun out of Stormy. They'd never seen him much with the girls, so they went below and routed him out of his bunk.

"You're big and hefty," they said to Stormy "and you're mighty good at catching whales, but we'll cut you out with the girls."

"Wait and see," was all Stormy would say.

They all clambered over the sides of the ship and rowed ashore in a whaleboat, and no sooner had they reached the girls, lined up in front of their igloos than the girls were swarmed around them, giggling and rolling their eyes. The sailors smiled their sweetest; they twisted their fine mustaches, blew kisses into the air and whistled, the girls were all so pretty.

But the girls were all eyes for Stormy. They'd never seen so big and fine a man.

Of course the sailors had thought of that, and they pulled out of their pockets the finest pieces of scrimshaw that each one had ever made, and offered them to the girls.

One got a pie-wheel, its handle carved in the shape of a serpent, and its tail curled up made the wheel for crimping the pie crust. The handle was all fitted out with a little, hinged fork for pricking the holes in the pie to let the steam out, and a knife-blade for trimming off the excess crust.

But Eskimos don't eat pie, and although it was a pretty scrimshaw it didn't make much sense to an Eskimo.

Another got a corset busk, all decorated in red and green and black with a verse inscribed on it, but Eskimos don't wear corsets and they can't read — at least they can't read English.

However, Eskimo girls are polite and all the boys but Stormalong had given them something, so before Stormy knew what had happened, each man had his arm around a pretty Eskimo girl's waist and they were wandering off in pairs, and Stormy was all alone.

But Stormy always had a trick or two up his sleeve. This time it was his boarding knife. He pulled it out, walked over to the nearest iceberg, and started carving in the ice. He hadn't said anything to anybody, but all the Eskimo men and women came out of their igloos to see what was going on, and pretty soon even the Eskimo girls and their sailor-friends crowded around, too.

Stormy just went on carving and didn't let on that he knew anybody was around.

When he had finished, he turned around, surprised, and made a low and sweeping bow, smiling a smile that captivated all the girls at once. Each one thought he was smiling specially at her. But Stormy wasn't smiling at any particular one. He just bowed low, and said:

"*My* scrimshaw for all the ladies of Kamchatka," or whatever the name of the town was.

Stormy had scrimshawed the biggest scrimshaw that anybody would ever see.

He had transformed that iceberg into a thing of intricate design, with bears and sledges, and dogs and seals and walruses and all the things the Eskimos knew about and recognized, worked into one gigantic design, with Stormy's initials "A. B. S." topping it all.

Just then the sun broke through a cloud and the rays glinted off of Stormy's scrimshaw in red, blue, violet, yellow, all the colors of the rainbow, so beautiful that all the Eskimo girls just left their men, dropped the little gifts the sailors had given them, and stared in wonder at the sight.

Stormy's scrimshaw never melted, and if you went up there today you'd see it just as he made it. When the sun is just right, the colored lights still blaze out from it across the sky.

Folks down here see it sometimes, and say its the Northern Lights, but it's really Stormalong's scrimshaw.

9

Stormalong and the Pirates

STORMALONG never forgot the stories his father had told him about pirates, and how most of them get hung before they die a natural death, so Stormy made up his mind if he ever came up against any of them, he'd do a little of the hanging of them himself.

Once when the *Gridiron* was out in the China Sea, they sighted four huge Chinese junks full of terrible Chinese pirates. The junks bore down on the *Gridiron* from all four sides at once.

Stormy knew that not a man of the crew would ever see the next day's sunrise if they fought that swarm of pirates when they came leaping over the ship's sides, because they outnumbered the *Gridiron's* crew by four to one.

Stormy did some quick thinking. The cargo of the *Gridiron* was mostly whale oil, but there was a lot of molasses from New Orleans in it, too, because of Stormy's appetite.

"Stove in the heads of them barrels!" Stormy shouted to the men, "and let the molasses run out all over the deck."

When these orders had been obeyed, Stormy and the men climbed up on the yardarms carrying ropes along with them. In an instant the slant-eyed pirates came swarming over the rail, their pigtails flying in the air and their huge curved swords in their hands. Seeing the crew all climbing up in the rigging, the pirates thought they had run from them, trying to escape.

"Choo chin chow!" cried the pirate leader, or something that sounded like that.

He must have meant "Go after them!" for the whole horde struck the deck looking as if they meant to go right up into the rigging after the crew.

The minute their feet struck the deck they went sliding and slipping and stumbling around and when they tried to pick themselves up, they fell down again. They rolled around and around until the molasses began to dry a little and then they got stuck like flies in the syrupy stuff.

That was just what Stormy wanted. He gave the order and the men up in the rigging slung down their ropes and lassoed all the pirates. Every single one was caught. Then Stormy and the other men climbed down and bound them hand and foot.

At first Stormy wanted to hang them to the yardarms, but they were human beings, after all, and when he thought on it, he relented. He kept those pirates as prisoners aboard the *Gridiron* until they got back to America. By the time they got to San Francisco the pirates were all pretty tame. So Stormy let them loose and they went off and settled throughout the country, founding the first Chinese laundries and the first chop suey restaurants ever started in America.

Stormalong the Farmer

STORMALONG was always a restless fellow. He was always wanting to try something bigger and better. He served on many ships in his time including the *Mary Ann* and the *Silver Maid.* He was once bosun on a Boston ship, the *Albatross,* and went to China another time on the *Lady of the Sea.*

Like every true sailor he longed to quit the sea, or thought he did, and go to farming. "Potaters," he said he would raise, "regular and proper spuds, not like the dead ones you get on this hooker."

"Another thing," said Stormy, "at farmin' all the hard work comes in good weather; at sea it's the other way around."

So, once when he had got himself signed up on a ship he didn't like and was pretty much disgusted with the way things were going, Stormy jumped ship.

"I'll walk inland," said Stormy, "until I find folks who don't know an oar when they see one."

He put all his belongings into a bag and slung it over his shoulder on an oar, and begun to walk west.

At last, out in Kansas or Idaho or somewhere, he found folks staring at him as he walked through the main

street of the town, and someone asked him what was that long pole he had over his shoulder and Stormy knew he'd found farming country where folks knew nothing about the sea and had never seen an oar.

He bought himself a big farm and planted it all in potatoes. But that year there was hardly any rain at all, and all the crops were dying for want of water. The sun shone down, day after day, and scorched the earth, and a few lazy clouds drifted overhead but no rain came out of them.

Stormy lost his patience for once. "They have water in those clouds," he said, "and they're just too stubborn to let it go. I'll squeeze it out of 'em."

He stepped up on the highest hill on his land and next time a good-sized cloud drifted over, Stormy just reached up and caught it with one hand, then put the other hand to it, held it over his potatoes, and squeezed. It had water in it, all right, and the rain fell over Stormy's potatoes.

That year there wasn't a potato in all the west, except what Stormy had raised, and he got a fair price for them, you can bet. But Stormy wasn't satisfied.

"At farmin'," he said, "it's all hot sun and pushin' a plow. Never a storm to make a man pull out all the best that's in him. My muscles was made for pullin'. Sailorin's the best job after all."

So Stormalong went back to sea, and a lucky thing he did for he signed up on the biggest ship anybody had even seen or heard of before. And it was a lucky thing for the Captain, that he had Stormy on his ship, for he couldn't have sailed it without him. It was too big for common sailors.

11

Stormalong's Ship

THE SHIP that Stormalong finally signed on was a ship worthy of his size. It was the *Courser,* the dream ship of Donald McKay, the most famous shipbuilder of all time. And it may be said, for Stormalong, that he was the dream-sailor of the great shipbuilder, as well.

The *Courser* was so big there was an hour's difference in time between her bow and her stern. Her rigging was so immense that no man could see all her sails at a single glance. It took five men, each looking as far as he could, to see the top of a mast.

Her masts were so tall the topmasts were on hinges and could be bent over to let the sun and moon pass. Even so, they often interfered with comets and meteors, and disarranged some of the constellations so much that the best astronomers have not been able to make much of them since. Her sails had to be made on the Sahara Desert, to find room enough for the sailmakers to sew them.

All the officers and the men on watch had to be mounted on horses, and some of the horse-marines were often too late for meals and missed them. Orders had to be given through a twelve-foot megaphone and then relayed through the megaphones by the ten mates.

She carried over 600 men and some of them never saw some of their shipmates from the beginning to the end of a voyage. It took thirty-two men to handle her wheel and Stormalong was the only one who could handle it alone. Turning it with one hand, he would help himself to a bite of Navy Twist with the other. When the Old Man called the men aft, most of them had to bring their compasses along to find their way to the quarter deck, and those that forgot them got lost and had to get their orders from their shipmates.

Young men who went aloft usually came down as graybeards. It took them so long to get up and down again, to reef a sail, that the *Courser* had bunkhouses and galleys built right into her yards so the men wouldn't have to come down until they got into a port or were jumping ship or signing off at the end of a voyage. Before the bunkhouses were built into the yards, the Skipper had to order all hands aloft six days before a storm.

The *Courser* could ride out any storm. She completely busted up several hurricanes and typhoons that came her way.

Of course, being so big, the *Courser* had to keep to the oceans; there was no harbor big enough for her to come about in. When she took on or discharged cargo, a whole fleet of ordinary ships would come out and transship the load.

Some of the deep bays in the coastline are merely dents she made in turning around. Now and then she rubbed off the end of a cape.

Once when she was blown off her course into the English Channel, she managed to squeeze through the Channel only because Stormalong thought of thoroughly soaping her sides. The Cliffs of Dover scraped every bit of the soap off her starboard side; and that's why they're so white now. The waves in the Channel are still foamy from the soap.

That trip she got out all right, but into shallow water, so they had to throw overboard all their ballast. They threw over so much that you can still see the piles of dirt. The English call them the Channel Islands.

Once, when she was down in the South Atlantic, a storm drove her right through the Isthmus of Panama, and that's the way the Panama Canal was really dug. The United States had sent a couple of men down there to make the survey, and a crew of men to dig it; and they took the credit, of course, but it was really dug by the *Courser.*

But Stormalong never liked life on the *Courser* as he had on the *Gridiron.* There were too many friends to keep track of, and 600 men always wanting him to relate his yarns over and over again made him long for the more intimate life he had lived on the whaleship.

So the next time the *Courser* passed within 50 miles or so of New Bedford, Stormy waded ashore.

12

Stormalong Takes a Rest

STORMALONG was getting on in years, and the time he melted all that ice with his breath took something out of him. Anyway, one sad day when his ship was out in the middle of the ocean, he suddenly took to his bunk.

Billy Peg-Leg sent from the galley a boat-load of fine whale soup, the freshest poached ostrich eggs, and all Stormy's favorite dishes to tempt him to eat. But Stormalong turned his face to the bulkhead and refused to eat or talk. All they could get out of him was a grunt, and he turned his face away from anybody who came near him.

When everything had failed, all the sailors agreed that it was the end of Old Stormy. Some said he had triple pneumonia. There were others who said he was just pining away because there wasn't anything else big enough for him to tackle. Another was sure it was simple homesickness, that Stormy wanted to go back to his old home in Maine, and ought to go. But Billy Peg-Leg, who knew him best, said: "They's a time comes in every man's life when he yearns fer something and don't know jest what it is he wants. Stormy's restless, he is, and he's jest a-pinin' away fer something he don't know what." But when Billy Peg-Leg took another look at his old friend, even he shook his head. "Looks like he's done fer."

Well, the word got around that Stormalong was about to slip his cable for Fiddler's Green, and there was a stirring in all the watery places of the world. All the undersea creatures (excepting, of course, the whales, who were breathing easy for once) began to murmur among themselves until there was such a sighing and soughing and moaning coming out of the ocean as you never heard. Even the shells, somebody noticed, if you held them close to your ear, were sighing. Frightened landsmen looked nervously at their weather charts and their barometers. Some kind of big weather was brewing at sea, but what it was they could not figure out from the signs. Then the Heavens began to weep; first just a few tears in a gentle little rainfall; then in great cloudbursts of emotion. Such squalls so plagued all the ships at sea that their captains said it was the most freakish and contrary weather they had ever encountered. Even wise old Davy Jones began to look for his keys to open up his locker for another customer.

The Captain of Stormy's ship, the *Gridiron,* was no exception. It ought to be enough that he should lose his best seaman; but now this weather! He was up before dawn pacing the quarter-deck and looking anxiously at the sea. Billy Peg-Leg said it was too rough to use the galley stove, so nobody had any breakfast that morning.

Billy had just come up from below, having had another look at the patient, when the Captain narrowed his eyes and said, more to himself than to Billy, "Hullo! What's that coming up?" Sure enough there was a sail just showing above the horizon. And then, as they looked another appeared and still another. And pretty soon there was such an armada of ships heading their way that all the sailors crowded along the rail to watch. Not only were there more ships than they had ever seen in one place, but the sea was speckled with sea creatures making their way toward the *Gridiron.* The Old Man thought at first they were whales and was about to dress down his masthead lookouts, when he recognized some of the ships.

There, making straight for the *Gridiron,* were the *Flying Dutchman,* the *Palatine Light,* the dead ship of Harpswell from Casco Bay, the slave ship *Mystery,* the *Mary Celeste* — all the ghost ships that sailors sometimes see; all the ships that had ever been lost, under a breath-taking spread of canvas. The marine parade was led by Old Neptune, the King of the Ocean, himself. Flanking the ships, like outriders, were sea horses, arching their necks, and mermaids with golden hair rising out of the waves.

Did I say led by Old Neptune? No, there was one ahead of even him. It was Pelorus Jack, the navigator. He had guided them all to the spot. He had brought them all to see their old friend, he was so concerned himself. They had come, as far as they knew, to say a last goodbye to old Stormalong.

You can imagine that all this commotion made some disturbance around the *Gridiron.* The poor old blubber hunter felt pretty shabby in such imposing company.

When all were lost in wonder at the sight, there came a new excitement. The *Gridiron* began to tremble from stem to stern. It was such a trembling that all the sailors leaped into the rigging for safety. They thought there was a collision with one of the ships, or maybe several of them.

Then all eyes turned towards the companionway, for there was the source of the new disturbance, and there was Stormy's head peering up at them and at all the excitement. The look on his face was something to see.

"What's agoin' on here?" said Stormy. "Can't a fellow finish his nap? And now that I'm up, how about a little breakfast?"

Then all the sailors and Billy Peg-Leg and the Old Man himself felt foolish, for they remembered that Stormy hadn't had a real nap since that time in the Arctic, and it took a good six months to get a good night's sleep for such a man. Furthermore, whaling in temperate latitudes was not like it is in the Arctic where the sun goes down and stays for a spell. Down here it sets each night and before you know, it's up again — and how could a fellow like Stormy get along on little cat naps like that? They weren't much better than the dogwatches, when for a spell the watch changes every two hours.

At the sound of Stormy's cheerful voice, the rain stopped and the Heavens smiled again, for there appeared, arched across the western sky, a beautiful rainbow. It was so vivid and lovely that all the sailors looked up in wonder at the sight. When they looked back, the sea was clear and all the ships, the mermaids and Old Neptune had disappeared, and even Pelorus Jack was gone. They had vanished completely. The *Gridiron* was alone on the ocean and there wasn't a sound to be heard except the waves slapping gently against her sides.

When all on board had gotten over their surprise and thought to welcome Stormalong back, he was nowhere to be seen. They searched the ship from keelson to maintop, but Stormy was not to be found, and as anybody knows a man of Stormy's size couldn't get lost very easily on a ship the size of the *Gridiron*.

"By Gorry," said the Captain, scratching his head, "I

do believe he's jumped ship again!'"

"And by Jiminy," said Billy, "without his breakfast."

None of his shipmates knew where Stormy went but they all believe in him still with all their hearts. And whatever sailors believe in, of course, has got to be.

The rainbow hung on for a time and all the sailors knew it was a sign that they must turn their faces away from sadness and turn back to their work and a new day. For the finest thing that any sailor can leave behind him is a happy memory.

As long as Stormy's friends stayed on the *Gridiron* they never ran across their old friend again, though they looked everywhere and inquired of every ship they met. But stories trickled back to them from all quarters of the globe.

One who had had some shore leave in the Mediterranean once, came back to tell about a building in Italy that was somehow tilted and tourists called it "The Leaning Tower of Pisa." "Stormy was there, you can bet," they all said. "He put that tower out of plumb."

One who had been through the Suez Canal said there was a place out there called The Red Sea, and anybody with any sense at all would know that it was red because Stormy must have washed his red flannels there.

One who went out to Australia described some creatures as big as a man that hopped around like fleas. They called them kangaroos, but it was easy enough to guess that Stormalong had been there, cast off his old clothing to get rid of the fleas, and bought himself a new outfit.

The Rock of Gibraltar? Stormy must have put it there to bottle up some Barbary Coast pirates, or for some other good reason. The Thousand Islands? Only Stormy could have scattered them about like that.

Pelorus Jack, the white porpoise, was never seen again, either, but the sailors were positive that if you could find Pelorus Jack, you'd find Stormalong. They had both just sailed away.

There's no end to the stories about Stormalong, and the sailors remember them all, and tell them over and over. And some day we may hear more of the marvelous things he did. For Stormalong was the greatest sailor that ever lived.

Glossary of Sea, Ship and Other Terms Used in This Book

aback — Backward against the mast, as the sails of a square-rigged ship in a wind coming from straight ahead.

aft — At, near or toward the rear or stern of a ship.

aport — To the port, or left, side of a ship, looking forward.

armada — A fleet of warships.

articles — Short name for the "Articles of Agreement" between the master (captain) and crew of a ship.

bar — A submerged bank (as of sand) along a shore, in a river or across the entrance of a harbor, obstructing navigation.

beam — Greatest width of a vessel; the side of a ship. "Beam to the wind" means the wind is blowing toward the side.

belay — To fasten a rope by turning it around a cleat or post. Often used by seamen in the sense of arresting or stopping, as "belay that chatter."

bend — To fasten a line or rope into position. Bending the sails means hoisting and fastening them to the yards.

blubber — Whale fat, from which whale oil is obtained.

boarding knife — A long blade with a handle, used in cutting up the whale. Sometimes used as a weapon in defending or boarding a ship.

bosun — Variation of "boatswain," petty officer on a ship in charge of hull maintenance and generally keeping things "shipshape."

bowsprit — A large spar projecting forward from the stem of a ship. On a sailing vessel a strong line or rope connects the top of the bowsprit with the top of the nearest mast for support and for holding sails.

bulkhead — An upright partition separating parts of a ship.

cable — A strong rope, such as the heavy rope or chain attached to the ship's anchor.

Cape Horn—The southernmost tip of South America, sometimes called "Cape Stiff" by seamen.

Cardiff Giant — A stone figure of superhuman size exhibited by showman P. T. Barnum, supposed to have been a petrified giant of biblical times. It was a hoax, but when the hoax was exposed it continued to draw huge crowds of paying customers who either wanted to believe or were curious about the trick.

carrick bend — A kind of knot used mostly in fastening hawsers together.

Carroll A. Dearing — A ship found abandoned on the high seas; the only living creature aboard was a canary in a cage.

caulking — Driving oakum into the cracks between the timbers of a ship or planks of the deck, to make watertight.

come about — To change direction or shift to a new tack in sailing a ship.

companionway — A ship's stairway leading from one deck to another.

corset busk — Here, a strip of whalebone used as a stiffener in a lady's corset, often decoratively etched or inscribed (scrimshawed) and colored with india ink as a gift to mother, sister or sweetheart.

cutting-in — The process of cutting up a whale.

Davy Jones — A sailor's name for the evil spirit of the sea; he presided over a "locker" which was the final resting place of sailors.

dogwatch — Either of the two 2-hour watches on shipboard between 4 and 8 p.m. Dog watches permit a change in the order of the watch every 24 hours so that the same men will not have the same watch every night.

dory — A small, flat-bottomed, open rowboat used by fishermen.

fathom — Roughly, six feet; the length to which a man may extend his two arms.

Fellowship — A ship that the early Swedish settlers of Delaware sent off to trade with England. She never reached her destination, was never seen again except one day in a violent thunderstorm she appeared in the clouds to be reaching port, then fell to pieces and sank just before reaching the dock.

Fiddler's Green — In folklore, the sailor's heaven.

fin out — (A whale) turned on its side; dead.

Flying Dutchman — A legendary ghost ship, supposed to be seen in stormy weather off the Cape of Good Hope. Her captain swore against God in a spell of foul weather and for his blasphemy was condemned to sail the seas forever without a port.

flukes — The two points at the end of a whale's tail.

fo'c'sle — Abbreviation for "forecastle," the forward part of a ship where the sailors live.

galley — The kitchen of a ship; the small cabin where the cooking is done.

hard aport — Turning the steering wheel as far to the left as it will go.

hawser — A large rope or cable used for towing, mooring or securing the ship. Strictly speaking a hawser is a rope from 5 to 24 inches in circumference.

hooker — Slang for a ship, especially an old or clumsy boat; from the general name for fishing vessels which use lines and hooks instead of nets.

hornpipe — A lively folk dance for one person, especially popular with sailors.

isthmus — A narrow neck of land connecting two larger land areas.

johnnycake — A bread or cake made of Indian corn meal.

keel — The main center-line structural timber running fore and aft along the bottom of a ship, to which the ribs are attached.

keelson — A beam fastened to the floor timbers or keel of a ship to stiffen and strengthen the ship's framework.

jewsharp — A small musical instrument that when held between the teeth gives tones from a metal tongue struck by the finger. Tones differ in pitch with changes in the shape of the mouth cavity.

jumping ship — Deserting.

Liverpool splice — An especially neat splice, a "long" splice in which there is little or no enlargement of the rope's diameter at the junction, from the English port that was a great training base for sailors.

maintop — A platform at the top of the lower section of the mainmast, for the convenience of men working aloft.

marlinspike — An iron tool, tapering to a point, used to separate the strands of a rope in splicing.

Mary Celeste — A ship discovered sailing off the coast of Africa with no one on board, an uneaten meal on the table. Her small boat was gone and the mystery of what happened to her crew has never been solved.

masthead — The top of a mast upward from the point at which the rigging is fastened to the mast.

Moby Dick — Name of the white whale in Herman Melville's classic story of whaling, "Moby Dick."

mudhook — A slang term for anchor.

Navy Twist — A kind of chewing tobacco.

octopus — An eight-armed creature of the sea, sometimes called a devilfish or cuttlefish; each of its eight arms has two rows of suckers by which it captures and holds its prey or food.

Old Man — The Captain: the term was not disrespectful on a whaleship.

Palatine — A ship wrecked off Block Island (13 miles south-west of Newport, R. I.) with two-thirds of her passengers dead from polluted water, the others sick and helpless. Her captain, after rifling her treasures for himself, set her adrift. On foggy nights some Block Island people say they can see the Palatine hovering in the mists offshore, giving off a ghostly bluish light.

pelorus — A navigational instrument resembling a mariner's compass, but without a magnetic needle, named for the man who guided Hannibal in escaping from Italy after his defeat by Scipio. Pelorus Jack was so-called because he "navigated" or guided ships into the harbor.

pig tails — braids of hair.

port — The left side of a ship looking forward. In early whaling days the term "larboard" was used to designate the port, or left, side.

quarter-deck — The afterpart of the main deck of a vessel, usually reserved for officers. The common sailor was not permitted there unless invited or assigned.

reef — To reduce the size of a sail by rolling or folding a portion of it and fastening it to a yard or boom.

scrimshaw — Etching or carving in ivory or whalebone, often intricately decorative, frequently useful.

ship anchor — To bring the anchor up and stow it away in its proper place aboard ship.

slop shop — A store selling sailors' clothing and other necessities. Aboard ship it might be called a "slop chest."

splice — To join two pieces of rope into one continuous piece by weaving the strands together.

starboard — The right side of a ship looking forward.

stem — An upright piece of timber, usually curved, to which the two sides of a ship are united at the bow. The bowsprit rests upon its upper end; the lower end is fastened to the keel.

transship — To transfer cargo from one ship to another at sea, instead of unloading and reloading at a dock.

try-pot — The huge kettle on a whaleship in which the whale's blubber is "tried" or boiled in order to reduce it to whale oil.

Wanderer — Outwardly an expensive yacht, below she was fitted out as a slave ship. She wandered, like Stormalong, from one adventure to another — from slaving to cruiser of war, to hospital ship, to peaceful trader; she was eventually lost off Cuba.

windlass — A device for winding up a rope or chain by a crank, used for hoisting the anchor or for moving other heavy objects.

yard — A long, nearly cylindrical spar tapered toward the ends to support and spread the head of a square sail. When in place it is secured crosswise to the mast.

yardarm — Either end of the yard of a square-rigged ship.